# On my way to School I saw a dinösaur!

## and other poems

# On my way to School I saw a dinosaur!

## and other poems

Roger Stevens

Illustrated by Nathan Reed

A & C Black • London

*For Sam*

**with special thanks to Graham Denton
and Michael Leigh**

First published 2010 by
A & C Black Publishers Ltd
36 Soho Square, London, W1D 3QY

www.acblack.com

ISBN 978-1-4081-2504-5

A CIP catalogue for this book is available
from the British Library.

Printed and bound in Great Britain by Cox & Wyman Ltd

# Contents

# On My Way to School
# I Saw a Dinosaur

On my way to school I saw a dinosaur
As big as a double-decker bus
And so I said to the dinosaur, I said
Please come to school with us

Teacher will be surprised
She'll think that I am bonkers
I told her I'd bring in an autumn leaf
And a bag full of conkers
(Not a dinosaur)

*I'd love to come to school with you,*
Said the dinosaur, *but alas*
*I fear I would be much too big*
*To fit into your class*

No problem, Mr Dinosaur
Here's what we can do
We'll widen the door, knock down the walls
And take the roof off, too

On my way to school I saw a dinosaur
As big as London Zoo
And the dinosaur said to me, *okay*
*I'll come to school with you*

# The People Carrier

When we go to school
We all squeeze into
The People Carrier

There's my sister Harriet
My brother Jake
Ed and Aziz
And Benny and Blake
Sarah and Clara
Ali and Dee
Ivor and Ivan
And Rosemary
My mate Billy
His pet worm, Clive
And Mum, of course,
Who has to drive

But there's no room for me
And it's starting to rain

I'll have to ride up on the roof again

# Billy's Worm

Billy has a worm
It's his special pet
Billy says it's the best
Pet he's ever met

Billy says worms are clever
But his is a little bit slow
By day it sits in a jam jar
At night it curls up in a bow

Billy's worm doesn't do much
But Billy thinks it's great
Its name is Clive and it's cute
  (for a worm)
And it's Billy's best mate

# Frog Class

I am in Frog Class
Ugly old Frog Class
Not Cat Class
Or Dog Class
But drippy old Frog Class

There's Antelope
And Elephant
And Leopard-with-his-spots Class
And Dragon Class
Flamingo Class
And clever, crafty Fox Class

But I am in Frog Class
The hide-in-the-grass class
The croak class
The joke class
Oh why am I in Frog Class?

# What We Did on Our Holidays

Miss Moss asked us
What we did on our holidays
And Billy said
He went to Mars
In a spaceship

Miss Moss said
Are you certain you went to Mars?
And Billy said
It may have been Margate

Miss Moss said
Are you certain you went in
  a spaceship?
And Billy said
It may have been a bus

Miss Moss said
What did you do in Margate?
And Billy said
We had to fight the aliens
To rescue the princess
From the terrifying monster

Miss Moss said
Did anyone else
Do anything interesting
On their holiday?

# What Teacher Did on Her Holiday

She flew a plane and looped the loop
She dropped her glasses in the soup

She climbed a mountain to the top
And left her glasses on a rock

She played for Spurs and scored a goal
She dropped her glasses down a hole

She went to the zoo and was chased by
   a bear
She lost her glasses down the back of
   a chair

She dropped her glasses in the sea
They were rescued by a chimpanzee

Where are my glasses? Miss Moss said
We put up our hands. They're on your
   head!

# Except for Billy

When our class lines up
It's a perfect line
Except for Billy!

When we walk to the hall
We are as quiet as mice
Except for Billy!

When we have silent reading
You can hear a pin drop
*And* you can hear Billy!

Miss Moss likes everyone
In the class the same
Except for Billy!

I think she likes
  him best

# Strange Sky

I am standing in the playground
And wondering why
The sun is shining brightly
But the moon is in the sky

It's as icy as the North Pole
And the wind makes me cry
The sun is shining brightly
But the moon is in the sky

And I am breathing smoke
Like a dragon trying to fly
The sun is shining brightly
But the moon is in the sky

Now here comes Mr Walton
Perhaps he'll tell me why
The sun is shining brightly
But the moon is in the sky

# Mr Bear

I clean the windows
And fix the clocks
I wear a red vest
And bright pink socks

*I'm Mr Bear*
*The caretaker*
*And I take care of the school*

I sweep up the leaves
And shovel the snow
I'm the first at school
And the last to go

*I'm Mr Bear*
*The caretaker*
*And I take care of the school*

I empty the bins
I tidy the store

I scatter the sawdust
If you're sick on the floor

*I'm Mr Bear*
*The caretaker*
*And I take care of the school*

I always smile
I never frown
If I wasn't here
The school would fall down

*I'm Mr Bear*
*The caretaker*
*And I take care of the school*

# Adding Up

One and one is…?
Two and two is…?
Adding up is easy
Let's try some more

Three and three is…?
Five and five is…?
Adding up is easy
Let's try again

Eleven and nine is...?
Add one makes...?
Adding up is easy
It's a lot of fun

Nine and ten is...?
Plus nine makes...?
This is getting harder
You have to concentrate

Now let's start with ninety-six
And then add on eleven
Do you think you know the answer?
It's...?

# Pick Me

Pick me, pick me
My hand is up high
Teacher won't pick me
Why? Why? Why?

And then when teacher picks me
My face goes red
Because the thing I was going to say
Has gone out of my head

# Nature Table

On the nature table
There's a sticky twig

A pebble, a mermaid's purse
A dead earwig

A fossil, some walnuts
A shell from the shore

A conker, a pine cone
And Billy's old apple core

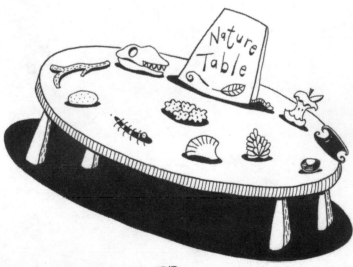

# Trees in Autumn

Trees in Autumn
Winds that blow
Golden leaves f

l

o

a

t

To the ground below

# Silent Song

I find
A small, white egg
Under the conker tree
In the corner of the school field

I hold
The small, white egg
In the palm of my hand
And look up into the tangled branches

The tree
Is empty and the
Small, white egg
Is cold

I think
There is a song inside
The small, white egg
That we will never hear

# Wind

The wind shakes the school
Like the beat of a dragon's wing
On a dark night

# Alone in the Classroom

Across the classroom ceiling
Crawls a shiny beetle called Bill

A fat, furry fly called Fred
Lands on the window sill

A thin, hairy spider called Sid
Scuttles across the floor

A boy who's been naughty called Me
Sits on his own by the door

I am staying in at playtime
Just me, myself and I

All alone with my regrets
And a beetle, a spider, a fly

# Billy's Painting

I wonder what we'll do today
Big sheets of paper
Stiff and grey
A rainbow of colours
In the painting tray
It's painting time today
HOORAY!

And Billy's picture
Is a bright red rose
In a garden where
A purple river flows
And the grass is red
And so is Billy's nose
And his hands are blue
And there's paint on his clothes
And yellow on the desk
And his book, where it shows
And his head is orange

And he's painted his toes
And what his mum will say
Goodness knows

And Miss Moss says
That's enough for today
I think we'll put the paints away

And Billy says
Is my painting okay?
And Miss Moss says,
Billy, what can I say?

Your rose is so real
It looks like it's growing
Your river's so wet
It looks like it's flowing
Your nose is so red
It looks like it's glowing

Now, I think we will have
To visit the sink
To clean ourselves up
What do you think?

# Robots

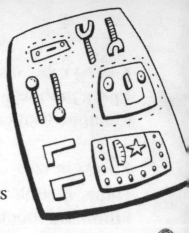

Today we made robots
R2-D2 robots
Old, bold and gold robots

Make-the-toast robots
Make-the-bed robots
Leaping, creeping, beeping robots

Robots that talk
Robots that sing
Cardboard-box-and-string robots

Kissing robots
Hissing robots
Monsters-that-glow-in-the-dark robots

Robots in cars
Robots from Mars
Kick-a-ball-about-in-the-park robots

And Billy's robot had flashing eyes
And Billy's robot was cool
But it jumped out of the window
And ran away from school

# Teacher on a Bike

We go to school in the People Carrier
And I like it
Our teacher has not got a People Carrier
Or a car
Our teacher has to bike it

She says a bike is brilliant
She says a bike is *brill*
It's fun on a bike, our teacher says,
Until you go up a hill
It's fun on a bike
It's ... fun ... on ... a ... bike
It's ...... fun ...... on ...... a ...... bike ......
Until...
You...
Go...
Up...
A...
Hill...

But-a-bike's-a-wonderful-thing-to-ride
Comingdowntheotherside

# The Alien

On my way to school I saw an alien
*Don't be silly*, said Billy

I saw an alien with two heads
*That's a lie*, said Di

I saw an alien with two heads and
    four arms
*You're having us on,* said Ron

I saw an alien with two heads,
    four arms and six eyes
*You're nose is growing*, said Owen

I saw an alien with two heads,
    four arms, six eyes and eight legs
*That's not true*, said Sue

OH YES, HE DID!
Said the alien

And everyone said
AAAAAAAAAAARRGH!

# Being Quiet

*Read the poem out loud, very quietly.*
*And as you read, get quieter and quieter*
*until you are whispering.*

It's all right
To be quiet
Just to sit
Sit and think
In the quiet
Of the day
It's okay
To be still
Still and quiet
Just to sit
Or to float
Like a cloud
In the sky
Or to drift
Like the snow
Or to tick
Tick

Or to tock
Tock
Like the slow
Ticking clock
Tick
Tock
Tick
It's all right
To be quiet
Just to sit
Sit and think
In the quiet
Of the day
It's okay
Shhhhh...

# Spook's Corner

Walking home
After school
When the sky
Has turned black
Past the three oak trees
By the old running track
There's a boarded-up house
That wears dark glasses
Its garden is smothered
With strange spiky grasses

*It's the spook, it's the spook*
*And it peers through a crack*
*Walk faster! Walk faster!*
*And never look back*

The spook lives there
And when you walk past
You must never look back
You must walk very fast
Or you'll catch the spook's eye

And he'll follow you home
And creep up on you
And when you're not looking
The spook
Will
Say...
BOO!!!

*It's the spook, it's the spook*
*And it peers through a crack*
*Walk faster! Walk faster!*
*And never look back*

# The Football Team

Number one
Here we come
Number two
White and blue
Number three
Pass to me
Number four
I'm going to score
Number five
Goalie's dive

Number six
Striker's tricks
Number seven
I can head them
Number eight
Shot too late
Number nine
That ball's mine
Number ten
Shoot again
Number eleven
It's a goal
Celebrate
With a forward roll

# Poems Don't Have to Rhyme

Miss Moss says poems
Don't have to rhyme
But they do have to skip
And weave and dip
And wheel and flip
And zoom and zip
Like an oojah-ma-flip
And stumble and trip
Or float like a ship
Or a boat on the lip
Of a wave or let rip
Or be cool and be hip
Or lie down for a kip
Poems have to have a good time
But poems don't have to rhyme

# Crying

Can you see the grey cloud
Up in the sky?
His face is so sad
He is starting to cry

# Rock-a-bye Baby

Rock-a-bye baby
In the tree top
When the wind blows
The cradle will rock
When the bough breaks
The cradle will fall
What a silly place to put the baby!

# Hey Diddle Diddle

Hey diddle diddle
The cat and the fiddle
The cow jumped over the bed
The little dog laughed
But not for long
Because the cow landed right on
  his head

# Helen's Lunchbox

I asked Helen,
What have you got in your lunchbox?
She said:

The crunchy taste of a summer orchard
The orange tang of a Spanish holiday
The mooing of cows moving slowly
   through the grass
The smell of freshly baked bread
And the salty scent of the sea
All wrapped up
In my mum's morning smile

# Billy's Lunchbox

I asked Billy,
What have you got in your lunchbox?
Billy said:

A squashy banana
An elephant burger
Dragon sausages
Mouse-flavoured crisps
A snail sandwich
Slugs and rice
And a dinosaur pie

Would you like a slice?

# Who Lives in the School Pond?

Water boatmen rowing home
Water spiders skip and scurry
Tiny fish dart through the weeds
Pond skaters in a hurry
Dragonflies with whizzing wings
Their turquoise bodies catch the light
Worms who live down in the mud
Fat old frogs who hide from sight
It's like a complicated play
I'd like to stay and watch all day

# Pond Dipping

Pond dipping
In the Spring
That must be
My favourite thing

I'm wearing wellies
So I don't get wet
And teacher has
Her big, long net

She's reaching for a frog
Look, she's nearly caught her

Watch out!

SPLASH!

Teacher's fallen in the water

# Something Smelly

On my way to school
I smelled a smell
It was a funny smell
It was a whiffy, funny smell
It was an iffy, whiffy, funny smell
It was a pongy, iffy, whiffy, funny smell
It was a yeuchy, pongy, iffy, whiffy,
  funny smell
It was Billy's bag

We looked in Billy's bag
And found a rotten apple core
A three-week-old lump of mouldy cheese
A Marmite sandwich covered in ants

And right at the bottom
At the very, very bottom
In the darkest, deepest bottom
Was a pair of Billy's pants

# Lucky Dog

On my way to school
A dog ran across the road
Right in front of our
People Carrier.
Mum stamped on the brake
The People Carrier went
Eeeeeeeeeeeeeeeeeeeeeeeeeeeeeek
And the dog went
Hooowwwlllllllllllllllllllllllllllllllll

The dog was lucky
And got away
But we were shaken up like dice
And Billy said,
Clive, my pet worm, has escaped

# The Invisible Worm

When we arrived at school
We hunted for Clive
Clive the invisible worm

We looked
Behind the seats
In our lunch boxes
In our shoes
In our socks
In damp places
In thin places

We looked everywhere
Where a worm might hide
But we never found Clive

I wonder where he is
And if he's still alive?
Has anyone seen Clive?
Clive the invisible worm

# Miss Moss and the Ring

Miss Moss has a wonderful ring
Made of gold and diamonds
And precious rubies
And sparkly glass
And she's always fiddling with it
And turning it on her finger
This way and that way
Like she's screwing her finger off
And then one day
When we were doing sums
She put it on her desk
And she had to leave the room
To see Mr Bear the caretaker
Because Alice's seat had gone all wonky
And when she was gone
Billy tried the ring on for a joke
And the ring got stuck
And wouldn't come off
And Miss Moss came back

And Billy had to sit with his hand under
  the table
In case Miss Moss noticed
And everyone was whispering and
  giggling
And so Miss Moss told everyone
To put their hands on their heads
And then on their shoulders
And then in the air
And then put their fingers on their lips
And Billy did it, too

But only with one hand
And Miss Moss called Billy out to
   the front
And said, Hold out your hand, Billy!
And then she said, Oh look, Billy,
You've got a ring just like mine,
And he had to go with her to the
   art area
Where the sink is
To get it off with soap and water
But it wouldn't come off
And so she called Mr Bear the caretaker,
And even he couldn't get it off
And he can do anything like get balls
   off the roof
And rescue the hamster
From under the cupboard
Anyway – Miss Moss said, Billy,
That ring is really stuck fast
I don't think it will ever come off
And you'll have it stuck on your finger
For ever and ever, amen,
And Billy started to cry

And the headteacher came in
And asked Billy why he was crying
So Billy showed her his finger
And she said, What's so unusual about
  your finger?
Because the ring wasn't there –
It must have fallen off
And Alice spotted it under the box of
  exotic animals
Like anteaters and zebras and dinosaurs
Which are made from old cornflakes
  packets
And things
And Alice said,
Can I try it on now, Miss Moss?
And Miss Moss took a big breath
Like she was going to explode
And we all waited
And she said,
I don't think so, Alice.
Now, let's get on with our sums,
Shall we?

# In the Shade of the Old Conker Tree

It's hot
So hot
In the classroom
All the windows are open wide
And Miss Moss says
I think that today
We will take our books outside

So we gather our things
And cross the school field
And there's no better place to be
Than reading a book
In the open air
In the shade
Of the old conker tree

I can hear a grasshopper singing
I can hear a bee buzzing by

I can hear the rumble of a plane
High above in the sky

I wonder where the plane's going
To a land that's far away?
Maybe a place where there's fighting
And famine
And children are dying each day
For we really are very lucky
And I wish that all children could be
In a school like this
Reading a book
In the shade
Of an old conker tree

# The Visiting Poet

The visiting poet says,
Howdy!
And leaps around like a kangaroo
We laugh and giggle and fall about
When he makes a joke about poo

His poems have wings
They fly over our heads
They are crazy and silly and mad
We join in and stand up and sit down
  and sing
And some poems make us feel sad

Then the visiting poet
Sighs and smiles
And sits on the visitor's chair
Has anyone got any questions?
And hands go up everywhere

So I ask him, Can I be a poet?
Can I write poems like you?

And the visiting poet says,
Of course,
If that's what you want to do

And I think about that in the classroom
What the visiting poet said to me
And I think that a visiting poet
Is a very good thing to be

# Going to School

As we went into school today
Miss Moss said
Billy, could you explain
Why there's a worm on your head?

# Happy Hat

When I wear my happy hat
Everybody sings
But when I wear my nasty hat
I hear such unkind things
So I threw away my nasty hat
Who would want a hat like that?

# End of Term

At last the term is over
And we all say Hooray!
And everyone is looking forward
To the holiday

Next term we'll all be older
And in another class
We learnt a lot of useful things
And time went by so fast

And so we say a last goodbye
Put on our hats and coats
We wave to Miss Moss at the gate
And a lump is in our throats

Because Frog Class is the best class
I thought you'd like to know
But right now – what are we waiting for?
It's the holiday
Let's go!